This book belongs to

....

....

Nita Mehta
PUBLICATIONS

Short Stories From
MAHABHARAT

First Edition 2005

ISBN 81-7676-046-3

Illustrations: *Nita Mehta* PUBLICATIONS

Artist: Rajesh Prajapati

Layout and laser typesetting:

National Information Technology Academy
3A/3, Asaf Ali Road
New Delhi-110002
N.I.T.A. ☎ 23252948

Published by:

Nita Mehta PUBLICATIONS

3A/3 Asaf Ali Road, New Delhi-110002
Tel: 91-11-23250091, 29214011, 23252948, 29218727
Fax: 91-11-29225218, 91-11-23250091
E-Mail : **nitamehta@email.com,** snab@snabindia.com
Website : http://www.nitamehta.com, http://www.snabindia.com

Contributing Writers:

Subhash Mehta
Tanya Mehta

Proofreading and Editing:

Ekta
Deepali

Distributed by :

THE VARIETY BOOK DEPOT
A.V.G. Bhavan, M 3 Con Circus,
New Delhi - 110 001
Tel : 23417175, 23412567; Fax : 23415335
Email: varietybookdepot@rediffmail.com

Printed by :

AJANTA OFFSET & PACKAGING LTD

Short Stories from
MAHABHARAT

ANURAG MEHTA

Nita Mehta
PUBLICATIONS

The Magic Potion

The Kauravas with Dhritrashtra

One of the most famous kingdoms of ancient India was that of the *Kurus*. They had their capital at *Hastinapur* on the banks of the river *Ganga*. When Pandu, the king of Hastinapur died, his eldest son was very young. So, his brother Dhritrashtra, a blind old man, became the king. Dhritrashtra had a hundred sons who were called the **Kauravas**. **Duryodhana**, the eldest of the Kauravas, thought the kingdom was his birthright and his father never said anything to the contrary.

Pandu had five sons who were called the **Pandavas**. Their mother was Kunti. The eldest of the Pandavas was **Yudhishthira**. The second was **Bhima**, followed by **Arjun**. The twins **Nakul** and **Sahdev** were the youngest. The moment the Kauravas set eyes on their five cousins, they bristled and a bitter rivalry sprang up. Duryodhana hated the Pandavas as he knew that Yudhishthira, being the eldest amongst them, was the rightful heir to the throne. But the Pandavas could do nothing as they were minors and all power lay with king Dhritarashthra. They tried to stay out of trouble by minding their own business.

Bhima troubling the Kauravas

Though the Kauravas hated all the Pandavas, they hated Bhima the most. Bhima was blessed with superhuman strength and was a prankster too. And often, the Kauravs were the victims of his pranks. He would shake them down from the trees when they were picking fruit; laughing uproariously as they came tumbling down. And if they tried to get rough with him, he would shake them off like little rats.

"We will get rid of him, once and for all," said Duryodhana viciously. "Without him, the Pandavas are nothing."

Duryodhana plots to kill Bhima

Duryodhana serving Bhima

The Kauravas made a wicked plan. They invited the Pandavas to a picnic. The Pandavas were surprised by this sudden friendliness but being good natured boys, they accepted with pleasure. Duryodhana specially told his cooks to prepare all Bhima's favourite dishes. Duryodhana, much to Bhima's astonishment, served him with his own hands, filling his plate up with meats and vegetables.

Bhima, being a simple hearted boy, never for once doubted his cousin's intentions. Bhima ate all that he could and when he was done; he got up and walked down to the sandy shore. Suddenly, he felt a strange buzz in his head and his limbs felt heavy and sluggish. The next moment, he collapsed on the ground. Seeing this, the Kauravas hiding behind the nearby rocks, emerged.

Let's go now

The Kauravas watching Bhima faint

"Quick! Cut some thick, strong vines," Duryodhana said to his brothers. "Tie him up tight. The poison is doing its work, but I'm taking no chances. Let's throw him into the river. With him dead, the Pandavas won't ever be able to lay claim to the throne." The Kauravas bound Bhima's feet and arms with tough vines and threw him into the river.

Kauravas throwing Bhima into the river

Snakes biting Bhima

The boy sank to the bottom and landed in a pit of *Nagas* or snakes. The *Nagas* looked at the strange creature in their midst and hissing with anger, they sank their fangs into his body. The poison flowed into Bhima's veins meeting the other already there and each destroyed the other.

Bhima opened his eyes and the snakes drew back in fear. Then he flexed his powerful muscles and broke his fetters. A few snakes tried to attack him again but he grabbed them and tore them into pieces . The rest fled.

When news of this reached the great Serpent King, Vasuki, he said, "I must see this lad who can make my serpents quiver with fear. Take me to him." The king and his councillors found Bhima ringed by dead *Nagas*. The boy looked up and stared unafraid at the great serpent king.

Bhima killing Snakes

Vasuki liked the courage he displayed and said, "You have shown great courage, my boy. I will give you a priceless gift as your reward." The *Nagas* led Bhima into a chamber where a number of small jars were kept.

"These jars contain *Rasakunda*, the elixir of strength," said Vasuki proudly. "Drink as much as you can. Each jar contain the strength of a thousand elephants." Bhima opened one jar and downed it. Then he picked up a second and a third. The *Nagas* looked at him with dawning respect. Nobody had drunk more than two before. Bhima emptied eight jars and this was truly a magnificent feat.

Vasuki, the serpent king

"Now you must sleep," the serpent king said. "Each jar takes one day to digest. I am afraid you will be asleep for a while. When you wake up, you can go home."

They escorted Bhima to a chamber with a bed and Bhima fell into a deep dreamless sleep. While in Hastinapur, Bhima's absence was a cause of worry for the Pandavas and their mother Kunti. Kunti quietly sent out search parties to find out about Bhima, but there was no news. The Pandavas noticed their cousins' goating faces but were helpless without proof, so they pretended they didn't know the Kauravas were responsible.

Bhima drinking the jars

Seven days passed. Kunti and the Pandavas were now sure that Bhima was dead. Far away from prying eyes, they wept into their pillows. The next morning, there was a shout in the hallway and Bhima burst into the room, eyes shining with excitement. His brothers leapt up, laughing, hugging and bombarding him with questions.

"O! What an adventure," said Bhima, his eyes dancing. Then Bhima narrated the whole story to his mother and brothers. "I killed a lot of snakes," Bhima said laughingly. His mother and brothers did not find the thought of his being poisoned a laughing matter. But they decided to put it behind for the best of the family. The Kauravas soon learnt that Bhima was back, stronger than ever. "He got lucky this time," Duryodhana said, "but there is always the next time."

The Princes get a Guru

One day, the princes were playing with a ball in a field outside the palace. The ball fell into a dry well and the boys wondered how they could get it out. "Duryodhana, why don't you jump into the well and retrieve the ball?" mocked Bhima. "Better still," said Duryodhana, "let us cut your head and use it as the ball instead," answered Duryodhana furiously.

As wild ideas went back and forth, they heard a mocking laugh behind them. Turning around they saw a tall, lean, brahmin standing behind them.

"So much for your *kshatriya* skills," said the brahmin mockingly. "Can't even get a ball out of a well; some warriors you will make!"

The princes with the Brahmin

The Brahmin throws an arrow into the well

"Can you get the ball?" the princes ask

The brahmin took off a ring from his fir
"I'll fetch both the ring and the ball," i
said the princes rudely. Ignoring their
stalks of grass. Holding them in his ha
hardened into small sharp arrows. Goi
with such force that it embedded itself
successions, each one piercing the othe
brahmin drew the ball up.

"Here is your ball, great royals," said the brahmin in a serious mocking tone. "Now, the ring!" The brahmin unslung his bow and shot an arrow into the well with terrific speed. The arrow tore down and bouncing off the rock on which the ring lay, flew up with the ornament on the arrow head. The brahmin caught the arrow as it emerged and slipped the ring on his finger. The princes looked at him wonderstuck.

"Who are you, sir?" they asked respectfully, bowing down. "We've never seen such skills-manship before."

"Doesn't matter who I am," said the brahmin smilingly. "Go and tell your grand uncle Bhishma what you just saw."

The princes ran back to the palace and charged into Bhishma's chamber. When Bhishma heard their story, a broad smile lit his strong, old face.

"This can only be Dronacharya," thought Bhishma. Bhishma was aware of the growing animosity between the Kauravas and the Pandavas. He believed that they needed a guru (teacher) like Dronacharya to put their energy to constructive use. Bhishma went to the palace grounds where he saw Dronacharya standing, leaning against a tree.

The two old friends embraced each other. "I knew it was you," Bhishma said. "No other archer could have done that."

"And I knew their story would bring you here," Drona said with a laugh.

"Drona," said Bhishma, "I want a favour from you. I want you to be the guru (teacher) of the princes. I want the best for the boys and the best means you. Will you be their guru?"

"Yes, I will," Drona said, "but they will not live in the palace. They will live with me and do as I say."

"They most definitely will," Bhishma assured him.

Thus, Dronacharya became the princes' guru. He kept them hard at work leaving them with no time for serious enmity.

Bhishma with Dronacharya

The Greatest Archer

The artificial bird

Drona was a stern teacher, tough on discipline. He left no stone unturned to train his pupils to become great warriors. Soon, even the clumsiest prince showed signs of promise. One morning, Drona asked the princes to assemble in the target ranges with their bows and arrows.

"Do you see the artificial bird in the tree?" Drona asked his students. "Yes sir," the students said in unison.

"The aim is to hit the bird's eye," Drona said. "You will each get one chance. Yudhishthira, you first."

What do you see?

Yudhishthira aiming at the bird

Arjun aiming at the bird

The eldest Pandava positioned himself and raising his bow, drew back the bowstring. But before he could release the arrow, Drona said, "Wait! What do you see?"

"I see the tree, the leaves, the sky, the bird, --------"

"Back to your place," Drona said angrily, cutting him short. "You have learnt nothing."

One by one, the princes were asked to aim at the bird and each was asked the same question. All the answers were like Yudhishthira's and with every answer, Drona became more angry. He invariably addressed his pupils with adjectives like dumbo, idiot, moron and the princes held their heads low in shame.

Arjun was the last to be called. As Arjun drew back the bowstring, he was asked witheringly, "What do you see?"

"The bird's eye," Arjun said, eye on the target.

"What else? The trees, the sky, me?" Drona asked sarcastically. "No sir, just the bird's eye," Arjun replied. "Come on, now Arjun! You can surely see the bird!"

"No sir," Arjun replied confidently, "just the eye of the bird." The angry scowl disappeared and a faint smile curved Drona's lips.

"Release the arrow," he commanded. The arrow flew with great speed and accuracy and hit the bird's eye. The bird fell to the ground with a thud. Drona's cold eyes raked the others who stood nervously shuffling their feet.

"You all have learnt nothing. Had this been war, none of you would have hit the mark. You would all be dead. Except for Arjun," Drona said looking fondly at Arjun. "Only he has learnt the most important lesson in archery : *The target is all that the eye must see.* Mark my words, Arjun will become the greatest archer the world has ever seen."

Eklavya's Guru Dakshina

Eklavya

One day, the Kuru princes decided to go hunting in the nearby forest. "This way we can test our archery skills as well," said Arjun proudly, as he knew he was the best archer amongst the princes. Arming themselves, they went into the forest accompanied by some attendants and a dog.

The princes with Eklavya

Suddenly, the dog raced ahead barking furiously. A red clad Nishada (forest dweller) youth saw the dog advancing towards him with threatening barks and growls.

Before the dog could close its mouth, the Nishada drew back his bowstring and quickly shot seven arrows into the gaping jaws, keeping them wrenched apart. The dog now couldn't shut its mouth. Yelping in pain, it ran back to the princes. When the princes saw the sight, they were stunned. Whoever shot those arrows had no peer in archery. He was in a class of his own! Seeing the dog, Arjun's face grew hard with jealous rage. "We must find this marksman," he said. "He is bound to be nearby."

A brief search led them to a sight which made them stop in their tracks. A slim forest dweller was shooting arrows with perfect accuracy into the heart of a target. Never had they seen such exquisite marksmanship. They watched him in silent admiration for a while and then Arjun finally spoke.

"Who are you?" asked Arjun. "I am Eklavya, prince of the Nishadas," the youth replied.

"Who is your guru?" asked Arjun again, unable to hide his envy.

"My guru is Dronacharya," replied Eklavya.

The name came as a shock to all. Arjun felt as if he had been hit by a thunderbolt. Then without another word, he turned and went straight back to gurukul. Arjun entered Drona's chamber and without saying a word just stood there. Drona noticed the tightly controlled anger and disappointment on Arjun's face and said, "Something bothering you?"

"You told me that I would be the world's greatest archer," Arjun said cynically, "yet today I saw a Nishada in the forest who makes me look like an amateur. And he says you are his guru. Tell me how can that be?"

"Take me to this boy," Drona said emotionlessly. Arjun led Drona towards the forest. When Eklavya saw Drona, he dropped his bow and humbly touched his feet.

Eklavya falls at Drona's feet

The clear eyes looked at him with unconditional love and devotion. But Drona's eyes revealed nothing as he looked down at the boy. At the far end, Drona saw a crude clay image of himself garlanded with wild flowers.

"How am I your guru?" Drona asked abruptly.

"Many years ago, I came to you and asked you to be my guru," Eklavya said. "But you refused because I am a poor forest dweller," he added sadly. "Yet, I never sought another guru as my heart had chosen you and would not choose again. So, I returned to the forest and made this clay statue of you. Every day, before I begin my practice, I pray to you and seek your guidance."

Drona listened to him with a cold face. He looked at Arjun who was quiet. Then he turned to Eklavya. "If I am your guru, you owe me my fee or *guru dakshina*."

Eklavya cuts off his thumb

"Anything," Eklavya said excitedly. "There is nothing I will not give my guru."

"If that is the case, then give me the thumb of your right hand," Drona said emotionlessly

The other princes were horrified on hearing this.

What was an archer without his thumb?

But Eklavya, without the slightest hesitation, drew out his hunting knife and cut off his thumb. Then he held out the bleeding member to Drona who took it wordlessly and walked away swiftly. The princes followed him in shocked silence. Only Arjun showed no sign of sorrow. Eklavya picked up his bow and shot an arrow. The arrow flew with amazing speed and accuracy. The skill was there but the magic that had marked it was gone forever.

Draupadi's Swayamvar

The Kuru princes graduated and left their guru's home to begin their lives in the world beyond. With the passage of time, Duryodhana's hatred for the Pandavas grew even more. He plotted to kill them and get them out of his way, once and for all. With

the help of his father, the blind king Dhritarashtra, Duryodhana persuaded the Pandavas to go to Varnavarta for a holiday. Varnavarta was a beautiful city on the banks of a river. Although the Pandavas knew that there was something afoot, they had little choice but to obey the king. In Varnavarta, the Pandavas and their mother Kunti were given a beautiful palace to live in. But the fabulous mansion was built of lac, straw bricks and wood - everything that could burn easily.

Yudhishthira noticed this and with the help of a miner, they secretly made an underground tunnel which led into a forest. One night, when all were asleep, Duryodhana's men set fire to the mansion. The whole palace was burnt down and news that Pandu's queen and his sons had died in a fire quickly reached Hastinapur. But the Pandavas and Kunti escaped through the tunnel unscratched. Once in the forest, the princes and the queen took off their royal garments and put on clothes made of bark fibre. They let their hair grow and the harsh jungle life toughened their hands and feet. Now they no longer looked like princes but ascetic brahmins who begged for a living.

The Pandavas realized that it was pointless returning to Hastinapur until they were in a stronger position. Duryodhana would only try to kill them again and his father would not stop him. The Pandavas and Kunti went to the city of Ekachakra and found shelter with a poor brahmin family. One evening, a stranger arrived at their door and Kunti offered him food and shelter for the night. Over dinner, he told the Pandavas that Draupad, king of Panchala, was holding a *swayamvara* for his daughter Draupadi. "That flawless beauty will bring all the monarchs of the land to Panchala. Lucky will be the man who wins her." The Pandavas listened to him carefully as he went on to describe Draupadi's beauty at great length. He told them how she was born out of the sacrificial fire, emerging full-born from the flames. "The king performed the sacrifice to obtain a son and got the princess as a bonus."

Draupadi

Listening to his words, the Pandavas decided to go to Panchala and participate in Draupadi's swayamvara. The next morning, they left Ekachakra and headed towards Panchala. Once in the city, they went to the palace where the swayamvara was held. The palace was filled with spectators and suitors. The commoners sat on one side, the brahmins on the other and in the centre, sat the kings on golden thrones. When everyone was seated, king Draupad said, "I have set a test. The man who wins the test marries my daughter. Near the pool, there is a bow. Directly overhead on the ceiling is a golden fish revolving at high speed. The man who wants to marry my daughter, must first string the bow and then hit the eye of the fish with one arrow. This he must do by looking at its reflection in the water." The kings grew tense on hearing this; this was not going to be easy. One by one, they rose and tried to bend the bow but not one of them could even string it. When all the kings had tried and failed, Arjun rose. He walked into the arena and picked up the great bow. The kings burst into loud mocking laughter when they saw the lean, young, bark clad brahmin handling the bow.

Arjun hits the target

Very unobservant men they were and nobody noticed the bowstring marks on both shoulders; the mark of the ambidextrous Arjun, the only one known to shoot with both hands. Arjun raised the bow with graceful ease, placed the arrow on the bowstring and drew it back. The arrow flew with amazing speed and hit the eye of the fish. The mocking laughter fizzled and was replaced with angry scowls. A book learning brahmin succeeded where all the mighty *kshatriya* kings had failed! In fury, the kings watched the beautiful princess walk towards the bark clad brahmin.

Draupadi looked at the tall, handsome, young man and shyly placed the garland around his neck. Arjun took her soft hand into his own and they proceeded to leave. At that, the kings rose outraged. "A swayamvara is for *kshatriyas*. Brahmins cannot compete!" they shouted. "Release the princess!" Saying this, the kings jumped into the arena fully intent on killing the young brahmin. Seeing their brother under attack, the Pandavas leapt into the arena placing themselves between Arjun and the murderously angry kings.

Arjun and Bhima fighting the kings

The attacking kings fell back in surprise as they were suddenly confronted by five well muscled brahmins, who behaved more like warriors! Bhima hurled the kings around like they were cushions and Arjun shot arrows with such accuracy that no serious damage was inflicted. Most of the arrows sank into the rear ends of the silk clad monarchs which made them even more furious. Thus, throwing everything into confusion, the Pandavas with Draupadi in the centre, slipped away through the other exit. When the Pandavas came home, Kunti, who was busy with some chore, didn't turn around when her sons entered. "Look at what I got for alms today, mother," Arjun said with a laugh.

"Share it equally among yourselves," Kunti said and then turned to face them. Her eyes widened in dismay when she saw Draupadi beside Arjun. "Oh, what have I done!" she exclaimed. "Yet, what I have said can't be taken back."

The Pandavas had never disobeyed their mother and neither could they do it then. Yudhishthira bowed and said, "We will obey you as always, mother." Thus, Draupadi became the wife of all the five brothers.

Karna - The Greatest Giver

After the Pandavas married Draupadi, they returned to Hastinapur. King Dhritarashtra divided the kingdom between his sons and the Pandavas, but the Pandavas got a raw deal. The king gave them the wild, barren land that lay beyond the forests of Khandava. But the Pandavas did not complain or protest. Through sheer hardwork and grit, they converted the wasteland into the most magnificent city on earth and called it Indraprastha. When Duryodhana witnessed their magnificence, his envy and hatred for the Pandavas multiplied manifolds. With the help of his father and his wicked uncle Shakuni, he tricked Yudhishthira into playing a game of dice.

In the game of dice, Yudhishthira lost everything - chariots, servants, cattle, wealth and even his kingdom.

Moreover, the Pandavas were sent to exile for thirteen years. The Pandavas completed their term of exile and returned to Hastinapur after thirteen years to reclaim their kingdom. But Duryodhana refused to give them their kingdom back. Everyone - gods and men - began to prepare themselves for a great bloody war between the Kauravas and the Pandavas.

48

Indra scheming

The guardian of the heavens, God *Indra*, who was also Arjun's father, naturally wanted victory for his son. He knew that the biggest thorn in Arjun's path was Karna. Karna had studied under Parasurama, the greatest of all sage warriors and acquired mastery over every weapon used by man. The mysterious story behind Karna's birth was a well guarded secret. No one suspected that Karna was the eldest brother of the Pandavas, son of the Sun God, *Surya* and Kunti. Later, due to fate and destiny, he became Duryodhana's most trusted friend. Karna's skill was as great as Arjun and he had the added advantage of the golden armour and earrings he was born with. With them, he was invincible.

"If I deprive him of Surya's armour and earrings, he will be no threat to my son. I must get them somehow," thought Indra. After thinking for a while, Indra came up with a very devious plan.

"Karna is a great devotee of Surya, the Sun God. All the world knows that he has sworn to give anything if asked, especially when he is praying to Surya. That is when I must strike. I will go when he is praying and ask for the armour and earrings." When Surya got to know of Indra's plan, he decided to warn Karna about it. That night, when Karna lay sleeping, Surya appeared before him in the guise of a handsome brahmin.

Surya appears before Karna

Indra disguised as Brahmin, asking from Karna

"Karna, I have come to warn you of Indra devious intentions. He is going to come to you tomorrow and ask for your armour and earrings. Whatever you do, don't give them to him."

"Who are you?" asked Karna. "I know you are not a brahmin. Are you a God?" Surya revealed his identity to Karna. Karna bowed low with folded palms and said, "I am truly blessed to behold you. But I cannot do as you ask. I have vowed to give anyone who asks when I pray to you and that includes Indra. I will not break my oath and if it brings death, so be it. I cannot live without honour." Surya tried to persuade Karna into changing his mind but Karna was adamant.

"If you must give away your armour and earrings then ask for his weapon, the thunderbolt, in exchange." Surya advised. He gave Karna his blessings and vanished. The next morning when Karna stood facing east, praying to Surya, a skinny, old brahmin came and stood before him. The brahmin held out his hand and said, "Give!"

Karna looked at the brahmin. He knew it was Indra in disguise. "What do you want?" asked Karna, though he knew. "Your armour and earrings," the scrawny brahmin replied, eyeing the objects with shrewd eyes. "I know who you are and why you are here?" Karna said sharply. "Some God you are? What will happen to your reputation if word get around that you, a God, petitioned a mortal? And you are not asking for a trifle, you are practically asking for my life?" Karna words had no effect on Indra who said nothing and just held his hand out. "Alright," said Karna, "I will give you my armour and earrings, but to save your face, give me your thunderbolt."

"So, Surya had warned you and yet you give," Indra said admiringly. "You could have avoided this encounter if you wanted. I don't know any man who would have behaved with such honour. I will give you my weapon but it will not kill the one you want it for. And you can use it just once after which it will return to me." Karna knew it was a bad bargain but he was no haggler. He drew out his sword and with swift clean strokes, cut the armour off his body, skimming it off like a butcher skins a beast.

Karna cuts off his armour

Then he cut the dazzling earrings off his earlobes. Thick, sluggish streams of blood flowed down Karna's body but his face showed no sign of pain. And as he gave the blood soaked golden armour and earrings to Indra, the gods came out to witness this magnificent act of courage and generosity. Scented flowers rained gently on Karna's head and stained red with his blood, fell to the ground. Indra received the celestial objects, head bowed in shame. "For this act of generosity," said Indra, "you will be known as the Greatest Giver of all time and the wounds on your body will heal immediately without leaving a scar."

Saying this, Indra vanished and Karna's wounds healed without leaving a scar on his body. Karna faced the sun and finished his prayers. In his face there was neither a trace of repentance nor regret.

Karna, the greatest giver

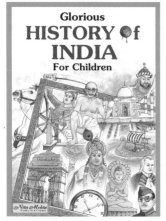
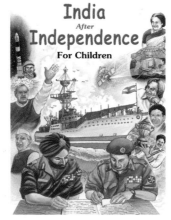
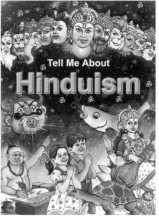